All Together Now

Edited By Donna Samworth

First published in Great Britain in 2020 by:

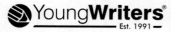

Forward Poetry

Remus House
Coltsfoot Drive
Peterborough
PE2 9BF
Telephone: 01733 890099
Website: www.forwardpoetry.co.uk

Printed and bound in the UK by BookPrintingUK
Website: www.bookprintinguk.com
YBAW0450I

Foreword

Expressing emotions, ordering the mind's turmoil or simply celebrating what's around them, poets and authors have used the written word to great effect for centuries. And when the UK, along with many other parts of the world, went into lockdown in March 2020 due to a global pandemic, we once again turned to the art of writing to help us through.

Around the country we were seeing acts of selflessness; acts of unity as people came together to show their appreciation for key workers and the NHS; and acts of sacrifice as people followed the rules of lockdown to slow the spread of Coronavirus.

We created Write to Unite as a way for people to share their optimism and messages of hope, as a way to focus their feelings of anxiety and frustration, or as a way to give thanks to those who made sacrifices for the greater good, working tirelessly to keep the country going.

When we launched Write to Unite we hoped it would give writers something to focus on during lockdown, and the response was beyond anything we had expected. Now we hope that this resulting collection of poems, prose and fiction will offer solace, hope, or even just pure entertainment to you the reader as you explore the experiences and emotions of ordinary people across the country going through something extraordinary.

Write to Unite reminds us that no matter what we face, we can get through it together.

Contents

Water Love

You were my water love. I saw you and didn't notice how deep like the sea your eyes were singing out to me. I didn't notice until I heard you speak that you were the one, the one to make me float. You're my water love, those eyes of yours they lift me up.

When you stayed by my side and did not rush off, I felt my heart begin to blush. You're my water love. Those eyes of yours they give me hope.

That day we slowly edged up to each other, close enough so that we could touch, our shoulders together, I knew that I was in love. When you got brave enough to touch my hand. A river was sent rushing through my body, igniting every pulse within me. You're my water love.

On the morning you left me the ocean tore me apart. It didn't make any sense to me why you had gone. But it mustn't have to you either because soon enough the tide pulled me back in and rested there with me. As you my darling water love returned.

My water love, I cannot wait to make a home with you in the real world so everyone can see how at home you already are with me in the deepest pit of my soul. You are my water love. Your eyes so blue, they keep me floating right along with you.

My water love. When all this is over, I want you to know, my love for you never faltered and when at last we get to return each other's embrace, I know it will feel just as electric as it did the very first time we kissed.

Hope Baxter

To Have And To Hold....

Staring out of the window, Diona could feel the panic rising from within. Damien had still not come home and he was usually home fifteen minutes earlier every day. She had tried calling, but he had left his phone at home.

The vivid thoughts of incidents and accidents that may have occurred were flying through her mind and her heartbeat was racing. She started to feel sick and sweat poured down her back. She wondered who else to call, but her mind was busy racing through snapshots of possible worse case scenarios. She shifted in her wheelchair trying to see further down the street but the neighbours' bushes blocked her view.

As she stared down at her phone, she tried focusing on who else she could call whilst tears blurred her vision. As one tear escaped, she heard a sound come from the back door. She froze in fright as thoughts of a burglar entering the house flashed through her mind. Her hands were shaking as she tried to dial and she dropped the phone. She bent forwards to try and get it, but the pain in her back prevented her from getting to it.

Just then the door opened and she quickly looked about for something she could use to defend herself. She picked up the remote control near her and prepared to hit the burglar if he attempted to come near. She could feel her heartbeat in her ears and as she raised her hand, Damien came through the door. She sat with her hands raised for several seconds, whilst her mind processed that she was safe and Damien was home and safe too. Then suddenly a wave of anger overtook her and she threw the remote. Damien ducked his head and looked back at Diona in shock.

"What's the matter, hun?"

Diona burst into tears as her body crumbled. It felt like she had just been deflated suddenly and she sobbed into her palms. Damien slowly came towards her, wondering if she had any other hidden remote controls lurking and confused about Diona's reaction. When he had left to take their son, Zach to school, Diona had been fine and happy to have some peace from Zach's relentless questions and stories. He came to stand next to her chair and slowly put his hand on her shoulder. She shrugged it off and then a few beats later, rested her head on Damien.

"What's happened Di?" He asked again hugging her gently. He knelt down so he could see her better and pulled her hands away from her face.

"I... I... was so scared...and you didn't take your phone... kept seeing you in an accident or something and... and I tried calling, but... but you didn't take your phone. I didn't know what to do. I... I... couldnt think and then I heard a noise from the back door and I thought it was a burglar and I was so scared... but, it wasn't and you... you came in and I got angry... so angry... I'm sorry. I'm sorry I threw the remote. Did I hurt you? I'm so sorry. It's all my fault. So stupid. Why did you take so long? I got scared. So scared."

As Diona babbled, Damien sat feeling very confused. He was only twenty minutes later than he usually would be back from dropping Zach off. He couldn't understand why Diona had worked herself up so much. Best thing to do would be to calm her down, he thought to himself.

"Di I was just talking to another parent, that's all. Now calm down. Nothing to worry about. You shouldn't panic over little things. You need to chill out a bit. Now come on, let's get your face washed and then how about we go for a quick bite."

3

Diona shook her head. She hated going anywhere since the fall that left her in a wheelchair. People stared and some even asked questions after questions and she hated being dependent on someone else for everything. Damien rolled his eyes and pushed her into the kitchen to wash her face. He gave her a towel and got on with making some lunch. Diona sat watching and feeling guilty. She couldn't understand why she couldn't just be calm and from the looks Damien was giving secretly, she could feel that it was affecting him as well.

That evening, she observed Zach's reactions and realised that he kept his distance from her. She realised she had been very snappy past few months as well and once again guilt chewed at her. She decided she needed to do something or she would lose her family as well as herself. She thought about what she could do, but felt like a block was in place. She felt Damien wouldn't be able to understand and she wouldn't be able to explain so she would have to talk to a professional.

She made an appointment with her doctor next morning and was lucky to get seen that afternoon. As Damien pushed her through the car park, she asked him to wait in the waiting room whilst she talked to the doctor. She saw his frown and knew that she must have hurt him as he had been through everything with her at her side and once again the guilt burnt her insides.

"Please. I'm trying to get myself back," she said to him as she held onto his hand hoping he would understand. He nodded his head as he pushed her through the door, still feeling a little hurt.

Inside the doctor's surgery, Diona was very nervous and she sat for a few minutes wringing her fingers together in agitation. She didn't know where to start. As the doctor watched Diona, he felt she wanted to say something, but needed prompting.

"Diona, is everything okay?" Diona looked up and shook her head. "Can you tell me what is wrong?" Diona shrugged a shoulder which made her wince and then opened her mouth.

"I... I don't know what to say," she finally said. "I think I'm going crazy." Tears rolled down and the doctor passed her the tissue box.

"Diona why do you think that?"

So Diona explained what had happened the day before and her reaction and her feelings and emotions felt like they were on a roller coaster. From her mumblings, the doctor understood what she needed and as he talked to her about maybe seeing a therapist would be beneficial, Diona felt a bit lighter and agreed to be referred.

As she left the surgery, she felt a tiny glimmer of hope that maybe she could come back.

Several weeks later, an appointment letter came through and as she mentally prepared herself, she also took notes down to help her explain her thoughts and emotions.

The day finally arrived and she felt sick and tired, but Damien assured her that she would feel better once she had been and if she cancelled, then she would never get the courage to go. He didn't fully understand how she was feeling and what was going through her mind, but he was trying and Diona could see that. So she took a deep breath and went ahead for his sake.

As she entered the room to her therapist, she looked back at Damien and he stood back understanding her need for privacy and she smiled her thanks. He winked at her and pointed to the waiting room, letting her know he was nearby. As she gradually opened up to therapist, she realised that it wasn't all going to go away after one session and she needed to put all her effort into it and she embraced that.

Several hard months of ups and downs, cheers and tears later, Diona could feel a light shining down the tunnel getting closer and closer. She had begun to sit outside for a while enjoying the sun and had had a lunch dates with Damien as well. She had decided to start attending a writing club and was enjoying it. "Baby steps," she whispered to herself now and then to keep her self going and felt like she was taking toddler steps now. Things were feeling a little positive and she was smiling more often rather than sinking into her own world.

The news of a deadly virus hit them in the middle of this progress and the country ended up going into lockdown. Diona was worried about the virus, but the lockdown was something she had taken herself under before anyway, so felt she would be okay with it.

However, little did she realise that this lockdown was going to be another struggle and as the days turned into weeks and then into months, she felt herself slide down little by little. She was able to talk to her therapist on the phone, but with everyone at home, she couldn't talk as easy and it became a strain to get thoughts across.

Thoughts of harming herself propped up and kept propping up like unwanted guests. She tried to block them out, but they kept coming back till one day, she used Zach's paper scissors to scratch her arm. As a little blob of blood, slowly seeped out she felt a rush of satisfaction and quickly hid the scissors in her recliner chair. She wiped up the blood and rolled down her sleeve, but as Damien walked past, she avoided his gaze and a rush of guilt overcame her and she started sobbing quietly.

That night, she told Damien what she had done and he checked to see if she needed medical attention but the bleeding was very minimal, although the scratch was a long one. He looked at her for a few seconds and wondered what to do or say. He felt useless and broke down.

"Why Di? Please tell me how to help you. I can't see you like this. Please. What if Zach had seen this? What if it had been worse?" He couldn't go on as thoughts of losing her swept through his mind. He held onto her and they both cried till Diona fell asleep. He quickly slipped out of bed and searched for the scissors and put them away. He looked around for anything else that maybe Diona might use and hid that too. He returned to bed and spent half the night watching Diona and worrying. He was going to watch her like a hawk now he vowed to himself.

Over the next few days, the lockdown began to ease, but the stress was ever present. They both made the decision not to send Zach back to school yet, as they both knew that Diona's anxiety levels would rise horrifically whilst he attended and Zach also suffered from asthma.

The days were all blending into one and Diona couldn't remember what day or date they were on till she got a call from her therapist asking her to come and see them. She was once again nervous and guilty, but Damien insisted that she attend and so she went.

After the first session, Diona could see she had slid down the tunnel a lot and once again she would have to start climbing back out inch by inch. It would be harder this time, but she knew she had to and she would, even if it took several years, but she had to get herself back or lose everything.

Naeema Rawat

A Scourge To Overcome

This world crisis is unreal to us who are cocooned in our homes, but the reality of it all is confirmed when the news is on and the selfless work on the front line is observed, in all its sadness, emotion and anxiety. Shopping has become bizarre and like a distant play from another world, as well as distancing ourselves, along the aisles of the store! Technology has become a good friend, and video calling a technological miracle of our age, unless like me your calls sometimes refuse to be received.

People especially those working from home are becoming home-schoolers and maids and indeed nannies and teachers all at once. As for the NHS on the front line they have become miracles and heroes of great bravery and patience and have my admiration and praise in huge barrowloads. I can't praise them enough, and hope they all get medals as they all deserve them. My two daughters work in care and they are working as hard as they can and I applaud them.

Our wonderful PM Boris Johnson is getting better in the ICU at St Thomas's Hospital thanks to the brilliant nursing and medical team he has, who are all working in perfect unison with all their skills and experience. The fact that some have lost their lives does not distract them from their vital job of caring for the patients who are fighting this terrible scourge that is COVID-19, and when this crisis is over they can bask in the glory that is surely theirs.

Jo Sparkes

Bird Boy

Jamie was sulking and sucking his thumb,
he had just had another big row with his mum.
For weeks and for weeks he had asked for a pet,
but his mum hadn't weakened or caved in just yet.

"No!" she had said to a cute Yorkipoo,
"'cause they don't wipe their bums when they go to the loo."

"No!" she had said to a Siamese cat,
"'cause they're nasty and mean and they scratch this and
that."

She'd even said no to a little white mouse.
"No way would I sleep with a mouse in my house!"

He'd tried insects, amphibians, mammals and fish,
but his mum flat-refused to grant Jamie his wish.
And then she had said something truly absurd,
"Jamie, why don't you adopt a nice bird?"

At first, he'd imagined a bright parakeet,
that would mimic your words like a song on repeat.
But Mum just meant pick one that's flying outside,
so he ran to his room and he cried and he cried.

Jamie felt lonely and desperately sad.
Life was much harder without his old dad.

He walked to his window and stared through the glass.
An ugly black crow hopped around on the grass.
Pigeons and sparrows flew round up above.
There was nothing of interest. Not even a dove.

And then...
Out of nowhere...
High up in the sky...
A great soaring red kite caught hold of his eye.

He tapped on the window... one... two... three,
but the kite changed direction and flew to a tree.
He stared at the bird till the dusk sky turned black,
and all of the while the red kite just stared back.

Later that night, as he lay in his bed,
thoughts of the kite floated round in his head.
The wind began howling, it started to rain,
but through all the noise came three taps on the pane.

He rolled up the blind and jumped back in surprise.
Behind the wet window gleamed two beady eyes.

He opened the latch feeling more than on edge,
but the kite didn't budge from the soaked window ledge.
For a moment the bird and the boy just stood still,
while the rain kept on lashing and drenching the sill.

The more the kite stared, the more Jamie felt sure...
that this bird was the same one he'd spotted before.

He lifted his hand up to stroke the red kite,
but the kite flapped his wings and flew into the night.

As Jamie was walking to school the next day,
he spotted the same red kite coming his way.
The bird flew above him until they reached school,
Jamie was thrilled but he tried to act cool.

His school friends would certainly laugh if he said
that this wild bird had got him up out of his bed!

When Jamie got home, he rushed straight to his room,
trying to spot the red kite in the gloom.
He tapped one... two... three on the wet window pane,
and waited to see if the kite came again.

And sure enough, soon came the taps, one... two... three.
Jamie was dancing and dabbing with glee!

This time the red kite had brought him a treat!
A fat juicy earthworm for Jamie to eat!
Jamie looked worriedly down at the worm,
the idea of eating it made his face squirm.
He picked up the earthworm to feed the red kite,
But the bird flapped his wings and flew off out of sight.

The following day the same happened again.
One... two... three came the beak taps on the pane.
The kite had returned with another small treat,
a dead little dormouse for Jamie to eat!

The thought of him eating it filled him with dread,
as he pictured the mouse in two slices of bread!
Jamie was dying to touch the red kite,
But the bird spread his wings and soared into the night.

The kite flew to school with him every day,
and followed him home again all of the way.
He came back to visit him night after night
and each time he brought an unsavoury bite,
earthworms and rabbits and lots of dead mice!
Though Jamie was sure that the Kite was being nice.
But whenever he reached out to stroke the red kite,
the bird spread his wings and flew off for the night.

One day at school it was Pet Show 'n' Tell.
The children lined up at the sound of the bell.
They had hamsters in cages and rabbits on leads,
And kittens and puppies of different breeds.
Jamie was sad he had nothing to show,
Without his own pet he just might as well go...

And then...
Out of nowhere...
So graceful, so calm...
The red kite swooped in and perched right on his arm!

Jamie's turn came to present his new pet,
he hadn't come up with a name for him yet!
He stroked the red kite and no longer felt sad.

"I named my bird Jackson.
After my dad."

His mum had suggested he find a nice bird,
perhaps her idea wasn't quite so absurd!
Jackson still lived his life wild and free,
but he came every time Jamie tapped, one... two... three.

Verity Mercer

Rebirth

The world as we know it is currently being destroyed,
By something that's near impossible to avoid,
The threat that is COVID-19 is growing stronger each day,
The Coronavirus is a lit cigarette and us humans are the ash
being discarded into a tray,
The virus is taking us out one by one, China, Italy, Spain,
when will it come to an end?
It's in these times we need to trust the government to
transcend and be our friend.

Even though the world is looking ever so bleak.
It's the silver linings and solace we need to seek,
Families becoming stronger than ever,
Everyone telling each other "This isn't going to last forever."
In this time of sadness technology has become a beacon of
hope to us all,
That not all is lost and even with the social distancing
measures we can still communicate and be together
standing tall,
So I urge everyone reading this to keep calm and carry on,
We will beat this and we will come out much stronger, we
will conquer the virus and the world will have won,
Stay at home, stick to government guidelines wherever you
are in the world and help save the people of Planet Earth,
This won't be forever, and if we all do our part, we can
successfully save the population and reach our new dawn
and rebirth.

Ethan Richard Connolly

My Nana's Healing Hand

It was April, I was seven,
Felt as miserable as mud!
Throat of nettles, hot as Venus,
Head and heart a *Thud! Thud! Thud!*
Then a letter, "Hope you're better
very soon my little pup.
Sent a friend to help you mend.
Lots of love, from Nanny Jupp."

From the envelope which rested on my lap
I could hear a very gentle *Tap! Tap! Tap!*
I know you won't believe or understand,
But out it crawled, my Nana's healing hand.

Waving at me very gently,
She jumped up to feel my brow,
And she grabbed a nearby flannel-
Cooled me down, I don't know how.
Made a fist and then uncurled it:
Solaroos of every shade
flew around me, brushing gently,
Making all the sadness fade.

"A solaroo? What's that?" I hear you shout.
A wingy thing that's cute and floats about.
I'd never seen one too, they're quite unique,
So shocked was I, I really couldn't speak.

Gave my scalp a soothing massage
Sending all my aches away.
Almost fell into a slumber
But the hand wanted to play.
Started tickling my belly,
Underneath my arms and chin.
Wouldn't stop until I shouted;
"Stop it Nana! I give in!"

What a cheeky hand to cause such utter strife,
But I've never laughed so much in all my life!
And throwing something else into the mix -
That healing hand began to do some tricks.

Rabbits hopped out from her knuckles -
First a black one, then a white.
Bunch of roses, scarf of hankies,
Then a bucket of delight.
Every colour of the rainbow
Splashed across my bedroom wall.
Wow! What magic! Now I'm feeling
not so very ill at all.

And what do you think that healing hand did next?
The strangest thing you never would expect.
It really was a healing hand you see.
And here's the proof of what it did for me.

Well, the index finger wiggled,
Glowing brightly 'til it shone,
Then it zapped above my body
'Til my tiredness was gone.
Bang! The wardrobe doors flung open
Urging me to quickly dress,
And we landed in my garden.
It was weird, I must confess.

Jumping high upon my orange trampoline
'Twas the strangest sight that I had ever seen.
Hand wanted me to play and run around,
So she gently lifted me up off the ground.

Whizzed with wonder on my skateboard -
Thought that we would lose control,
And although it wasn't legal
What a simply perfect goal!
Who'd have thought that pogo-sticking
Worked as well without two legs,
And that there would be such fun
In freeing trousers from their pegs?

But I realised the hand needed to leave
When she started to retract inside her sleeve.
She didn't want to go though, I could tell,
But her job was done, and she had made me well.

Then I saw... another hand... and
Then another three or four,
'Til my garden fence was littered
With a hundred hands or more.
Different sizes, different ages,
Some with nails as bright as day;
Rings on fingers, warts and wrinkles,
What a beautiful display.

First they bowed to say "Well done for being brave"
And then every hand gave me a goodbye wave.
Heard the clapping rise like thunder from the skies
Then they disappeared before my very eyes.

But Nana's hand was left with me to wipe away my sadness,
And squeeze my cheeks to make me grin and laugh at all
the madness.
Our hands pressed close together, it was time to say
goodbye,
So with one last tussle of my hair, she danced into the sky.

When Nana came to visit some months later
From her home on the other side of the equator,
She said how glad she was that I was better,
And asked if I had got her Get Well letter.

I said I had, and gave my thanks so she would understand
With a kiss not planted on her cheek, but on her lovely hand.
We held each other close, knowing however far apart,

A hand can't always reach a hand, but a heart
will always... always
reach a heart.

Dawn Horne

Victory Will Be Over The Rainbow

Living has truly become a burden of darkness to our nation
For this treacherous plague it still ceases to take the entire population
Nobody realised how traumatic it was until the spread increased
I truly honour those who continue the fight and the beautiful souls that sadly has deceased
In this mentally life-changing experience be a reflection on our hearts to fight
Our actions against this tragedy will be storytelling to the world to keep shining 'a light'
Thank you to our incredible NHS heroes who are on the frontline continuing to be strong as ever
Although this challenge seems to be in darkness, we will conquer this head-on together
I clap to all the keyworkers who are committed to supporting this pandemic despite the fear
Let's stand together and give these amazing people a huge cheer
Strength empowers over the darkest paths we come to face
Become an anchor of reassurance for the human race
Over the rainbow there will be a victory of a gold that our lives cannot buy
Let harmony be upon the angels who's heart was guided to forever shine in the sky.

Melissa Patty

The Flowers Will Once Again Bloom

When my husband and I were dating, he would occasionally receive packages in the mail. They came in a box, no bigger than a shoebox, his name and address hand-scribbled in ink pen. Once opened, the package would reveal an assortment of snacks. It might have packs of gum, individually-wrapped Rice Krispie treats, and, my favourite, baggies of Cheetos. Yep. I'm talking about the baggies you use to package up food for storage or for keeping fresh in lunch boxes.

At this point, my husband was in his early 20s. He had two undergraduate and one graduate degree under his belt, and was a couple of years into his career. But, these packages still came. They were a symbol of love and a beautiful way of showing he'd been in her thoughts.

You see, these boxes were lovingly packed by his grandma, who lived in the Texas panhandle, more than a seven-hour drive from his Houston apartment. Her gift was kind, thoughtful, and such a sweet way to show how much she cared. Instantly, I was overcome with warmth and connection to a woman I came to respect and love so dearly.

And it is this woman who I have been thinking about during this time of social distancing and living life outside of the norm. In these memories, I find my strength.

Norma Steinhauser was born in 1912 around Bartlett, TX, her family relocating during her childhood to the Lubbock, TX area. Marrying in the early 1930s and living the life of a farmer in the southern plains of the United States, she was not only witness to tough times due to the Great Depression that swept the world, but also to the Dust Bowl that sent many fleeing to the west.

But she and her husband, Edmund, stayed. They endured unexplained black storms of dust that choked not only the land, but also the people and livestock. She learned to be frugal. To get by on very little, and to save for when times may be tough. My husband often jokes about how one can really get by on a 15-watt light bulb. But, most importantly, she learned to hold her head high and keep going. It was a practice that would hold true for her for the rest of her life. I told my husband that his beloved grandma had been on my mind lately as we find ourselves living a new normal for an unknown length of time. He grabbed a copy of the book *The Worst Hard Time* by Timothy Egan and immediately fingered to a section for me to read so that I may get an understanding of just what the farming community lived through during the Dust Bowl. In that section, I found the following passage:

Hazel tried to get her cousins to see beyond 1932. Hazel believed in tomorrow perhaps more than any member of her extended family. She had seen hailstorms that collapsed a dugout; she had seen lightning scatter a horse team, and a prairie fire come right up to the house. This arid, tortured stretch of slow time - it was just another trial, and then the purple verbena would bloom again, and the labors of No Man's Land could mean something, surely. Look at all they had accomplished in half a generation's time: going from dirt-dwellers with nothing to making a decent living. To return to subsistence was something a Lucas could put up with. The best way around the ubiquity of despair was to think of new life. Hazel wanted to start a family, but who could bring a baby into a world without hope?

That's why you had to banish the negative thoughts, she said. She could will a positive day.

The woman I met soon after my husband and I started dating in 1999 was someone that had lived through unbelievable challenges. She never let go of her sense of saving up for a rainy day and always had treasures buried deep in her freezer. But though she was weathered by the years and the trials of life, her heart and love only grew deeper. She was always such a shining light, and would never, EVER sit down until she knew you were stuffed to the gills and had a Twinkie to take back home with you. Just in case.

So though life may be a little scattered right now, and though we find ourselves working through new challenges, perhaps think of Grandma and the other farmers who kept their families close all while withstanding the scary and unexplained phenomena that passed through the southern plains. Believe in tomorrow. Hold on to a new day. And know that the flowers will once again bloom.

Erin Stolle

Team 214 Is Awesome

Team 214 is my class at my amazing school, Wickliffe Progressive Elementary. Wick is amazing because we are a community of learners who really care about each other. Mr Collaros, my first principal at Wick, asked us to keep the three Cs in mind as we worked together. The three Cs are Community, Compassion, and Civility. He died about a year ago of cancer. Although he is no longer with us physically, he is with us in spirit.

We have a new principal now. Her name is Mrs Evans. She was chosen to be our new leader because we know that she will keep the spirit of Mr C and the three Cs alive so that Wick stays awesome.

My class exhibits the three Cs by caring about each other. We try to honour and respect each other's needs daily. We are kind to one another. We make sure everyone is included and heard. In our classroom, each teammate has a responsibility to participate in our community. We set our norms together, and we hold each other accountable, yes, even me the teacher. We know that nothing is more important, nothing than the relationships we have with each other. When we damage a relationship, we repair it.

Shelly Hughes

Coffee Morning Mum

As I walk through the hallway and step into the kitchen, I am greeted by a warm and bright welcome. The sun beams through the window, touching my skin, enveloping me in rays of vitamin D. My caramel skin needs some of that goodness! I look to the right wall and the clock says 6:30am. Once upon a time, 6:30am would be when I would be crawling into the house, and now it's when my day starts – who figured?

On the window sill, two of my green plants bask in the heat, I look at their dark green leaves and smile. Wow, I have kept these two plants alive for eight months, I believe I am in 'plant mama' territory now. Keeping plants hydrated is not as easy at you think. Even I forget to drink my H20 without coffee in it.

I top up the kettle and switch it on. Opening the cupboard above my head, I reach for my favourite mug. Now only people of a certain age can relate to this, but mugs are a real source of joy. Yes, people who don't throw shapes on the dancefloor anymore have to find other little nuggets of happiness. My carefully selected mugs are in pairs, two by two they sit together in Harpreet's Ark. Except one, which used to be a pair but I am really clumsy when washing the dishes. In fact, someone as clumsy as me should not find joy in pairs, because my annoyance, when I smash one is self-inflicted! The kettle hums, wobbles, and then flicks off. Mmm, I am one step closer to my morning ritual.

I spoon the coffee granules in, and top the mug up with boiling hot water. As I like my coffees shaken not stirred, I shake my favourite oat milk in the carton.

It's almost like a mini bingo-wing workout, Tom Cruise in Cocktail springs to mind. I shake vigorously for around 10 seconds. By the 7th second, I swap arms because it's far too early to be moving the body like this. I twist the lid and pour a luscious, bubbly flow of oaty goodness in to my coffee. A quick swizzle with the spoon and boom! My morning HIIT workout is Peruvian and full-bodied with dark chocolate undertones.

I walk into the lounge with my mug in hand, scanning the room for the TV remote. It isn't in its usual spot, so I look at both sofas to see if it is there. No remote in sight, this is annoying. I walk over to one sofa and put my hand down the sides. No remote. I walk to the other sofa, lift the cushion, and yes, there it is. I don't know why my husband can't just put it back on the side table where it should go. Oh...hang on... he went to bed at 9:15pm and I stayed up watching Friday Night Dinner. Well... I was tired, so it's an easy mistake to make.

Okay here we are, I am in my favourite seat on my soft brown Chesterfield sofa. The TV is on and it falls on to a repeat of Gavin and Stacey, which I will gladly watch again. I lift the mug to my mouth and then Uncle Bryn appears on the screen. He is my favourite character, so I hold the mug still and chuckle, trying not to shake and spill the drink on myself. Oh, he's so silly! I lift the mug slowly to my mouth again. It almost touches and my lips and then I hear a small voice. A small familiar voice. Saying a word I really don't want to hear right now.

"Mummy!" I stay silent, in the hope that she will forget that she wants me. A few seconds pass. "Mummmy!" The littler voice shouts louder and elongates at the end. I detect a barrel-load of determination in her tone.

Perhaps, she'll opt for Daddy instead, who sleeps soundly in his bed. Well... I was going to say like a baby, but 'like a Daddy' is a much better description. And then she says those four little words. The words that makes every parent mutter quietly in their best French... "MUMMY, WIPE MY BUUUUM!"

And just like that, the peace and tranquillity of the morning evaporates into thin air. I mutter, sigh, huff and puff, finally accepting that I can either keep breathing irregularly or just go and clean the little bottom that I bought into this world. Goodbye coffee, maybe I'll microwave you in 45 minutes, or maybe you'll end up being poured down the sink. Either way, you deserved better.

Harpreet Kanda

I'm Not A Poet!

I was nominated. One of three,
To put pen to paper to help spread positivity.
I am NOT a poet, but this once I'll write poetry,
A lot of us are doing things we don't do usually.

We've slowed down. We've taken stock.
We've found out what matters... and what does not.

We're spending more time with our family,
And FaceTiming those that, for a while, we can't see.

We're teaching our children, and learning ourselves,
Every moment more precious, more heartfelt.

We're enjoying our homes. Chilling. Relaxing.
We're finally present in a world that was so damn
distracting.

We're feeling more a part of our community,
Putting painted rainbows in our windows for all to see.

Times are crazy, mental and there are reasons to be sad,
But you have to remember that things aren't ALL bad.
If we're here for each other, we'll be alright,
So that is why we should ALL write to unite!

Morgan Walton

Our Long-Suffering Planet

When we first heard of this new virus in China it wasn't a big deal. Daily events once taken for granted such as grocery or clothes shopping, visiting relatives, eating out with friends or going to the gym or the swimming pool went on as normal and it was almost as though it was out of sight, out of mind. That's in China, not here.

Then, everything changed so rapidly that we still haven't adjusted to our new living and working conditions almost three months since lockdown began. Queueing for every little nuance or necessity has not become easier with time. Home haircuts are the new trend everyone is doing.

Working remotely from home is the new norm. We all miss seeing our friends whenever we felt like it, travelling to our grandparents' houses to check in on them and have a cup of tea.

We all miss the feeling of freedom when we step outside which now feels like the smallest relief, as if we are living in a giant hamster cage. We cannot travel. We can hardly go outside. We all feel trapped in our own homes despite this being where we should feel our most comfortable and be able to relax after a hard day's work. Now there is no work/life separation so that feeling of slight relief doesn't come.

However, despite all the negativity and emotions and mental health impacts which have mounted on top of us for these past few months, there is also good. To me it feels like our planet has finally had a chance to breathe for the first time in millions of years.

Why? Climate change.

What does this have to do with COVID-19? Humans do.

You see, the impact which this global pandemic has had on humanity is almost the opposite of the impact it has caused on our planet. Whilst we have all been shuttered away inside, our planet has taken large steps by itself to recovery. The pollution has decreased significantly and so have greenhouse gases, meaning that our impact on the ozone has lessened drastically for the first time since before the industrial revolution. Our heavily polluted oceans and rivers and lakes have all cleared and species which haven't inhabited some areas for hundreds of years have been revelling in this newly rejuvenated environment.

I'm sure we all remember the jellyfish in the crystal clear waters of the canals in Venice which before were so contaminated that no life was possible there. That hauntingly beautiful image will stay with me forever as a prime example of what humans have done to our planet.

In three months of human absence the world has begun a long healing process which we must uphold in order to ensure that future generations can enjoy the raw beauty that only our planet can offer. To me this virus has been a wake-up call. Climate change is real and it is happening all around us. The suffering we have felt during this lockdown is nothing in comparison to the suffering our planet has endured since human civilisation began.

Now, as we slowly ease into a new sense of normality and restrictions are lifted, we must remember this lesson and help our planet to transform once more into the beautiful green and blue planet it is supposed to be.

Isla MacKinnon

Strange Times

2020 was just beginning
And everything was going fine
Until a tiny killer virus
Crossed the Chinese border line

It spent most of its time over there
But spread really fast, which was new
And eventually it got to Britain
But we didn't know quite what to do

Some people were really panicking
Others just thinking whatever
Queuing up to buy cheeseburgers
Like McDs is closing forever

Everybody should stay indoors
Be respectful kind and smart
Give that house a real good tidy
And try keep those kids apart

There'll be plenty for them do though
Lots of homework and stuff online
They can try baking or drawing or reading
Or PE with Joe, Live at 9!

The government are doing well
Not one of them seems a novice

Awaiting daily updates
Form everyone's new best friend Boris!

Everyone warned to be extra careful
And think about how they live
Was I the only one freaking out
When Tom hanks tested positive?

Yet Ant and dec still carried on
They really are great lads
And even though they had no audience
Someone still won the ads!

The supermarkets are all empty
Like they've vanished into a big black hole
No pasta eggs or even tins
And where's all the toilet roll?

If you're feeling a bit ill
And the test has come back yes
There really is no Need to worry
Cos we've got the best NHS

We've got great healthcare workers
They really are the best
Doctors, nurses, cleaners, drivers
Not to mention all the rest

A quick note For all you couples out there
Spending more time together these days

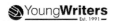

spare a thought for us midwives
And please be safe in ALL your ways

And During this time remember
More love might need to be shown
To those you know who are vulnerable,
Elderly, scared or alone

So before things go even further
And everyone starts to go nuts
Let's all work together
And kick these viruses' butts!

The sooner we follow advice
The quicker things will recover
so please Stay inside. Wash your hands
and look after each other.

Charis Fage

The Berserect's Arch

Lying near a lake with its trunk in the water, a tall fine figure comes and kneels next to the Berserect. The fine figure drapes its fingers through the water and the creature watches as the ripples reach to the other side. It looks up to the figure. The figure gently smiles. There's a longing in the face of the Berserect, a feeling that needs to be found. The figure moves closer and rests its hands under its jaw and lifts it slightly. The warm hands begin to rekindle a connection.

"Did you fall?"

"Quite some time ago, and now I'm lost."

The figure reaches down into its long coat and retrieves a round ball. It places it next to the Berserect.

"Then you will need this."

The ball rolls gently, side to side. As it slowly begins to settle, the figure starts to glide away.

"...but wait. What is it?"

The figure turns slightly and smiles.

"It's the guiding hope. And in it, you will find your next adventure."

Georgina Cooper

Snatching Victory From The Spores Of Defeat

Folk say I'm far too negative
Too controversial and crude
That I'm too obsessed with politics
And holidays, beer and food
So now I'm confined to quarters
With no certain end in sight
I'm penning something positive
Good over evil – dark into light

Never have I seen so many pristine
Perfectly tended gardens
Never have I seen so many cars
On drives – but no traffic wardens
Never have I seen so many neighbours
Finally start to talk
And never have I seen so many people
Cycle, jog or walk

I'm working the hours that suit me
But the work gets done that way
And whenever the weather permits it
I am taking long walks each day
I've discovered paths and bridleways
That I never knew existed

And people have started to say hello,
When they would have once resisted

I've seen horses in the fields
I've seen herons in the sky
I've seen mallards in the river
I've seen beautiful butterflies
I appreciate the sunshine
And those little pleasures of life
And now we've got no football... well
Conversation is rife

The main roads are deserted
And pollution's going down
As people help the needy
Community spirit's back in town
As half a million volunteers
Have stepped up to the mark
To counter greed and selfishness
And that panic buying lark

We've learned that public services
Are essential to us all
And that funding them is no bad thing
Cos they help the vulnerable
And rather than cheering football teams
Or clapping some star's address
We're applauding our genuine heroes
The marvellous staff of the NHS

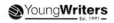

Never have I heard so many lawnmowers
Buzzing throughout the day
Never have I heard so many children
In their gardens at play
We're busy snatching victory
From the spores of defeat, you bet
But the best thing of all just has to be
That we haven't all caught it yet!

Rich Jones

Hope

Lows are never forever, there's always hope on
which to hold,
There's always love to embrace to make these
nights less cold.
Birdsong's morning chorus will warm the chill of
the early air,
And the stars will twinkle brighter when the darkness is
too much to bear.

Tears will eventually fade, these empty spaces
will become full,
And laughter's notes will echo to shatter this lonely lull.
We'll make eternal memories to cherish when
freedom reigns,
I'll promise to hold you tighter once we are free of
all these chains.

In this world of currency, treasure the priceless;
love and health,
Let's create a world of consideration, no thoughts
of just oneself.
For now, let's allow Nature to flourish in this time of peace,
While clouds float and rivers flow; listen to the
Earth breathe...

Byron Tobolik

COVID-19

Well this is all new, so what can I say?
A new pandemic, in our world today.
A virus that has attacked our human race
So many people dying all over the place

The sorrow for ones who have lost
All those people who are paying the cost
The fear, the panic and the undeniable grief
The whole wide world in a state of disbelief

All those workers, working on the front line,
Trying to beat this thing with very little time
There are no words to show our thanks
But know we stand behind you in our ranks

Through all this pain and sorrow, I must confess
A little hope my way I need to address
For those of you who haven't thought
There are a few silver linings that need to be taught.

I'm spending time with my children, be it in a different way
Seeing how hard it is to be a teacher, every single day
I'm learning to cook, well trying at least
Not quite ready for a banquet or feast

For someone who very rarely goes out
Now people can see what I'm really, about

Group video chats with family and friends on your phone
To help you know that you are never truly alone

This is where some people you know really shine
Those who make sure others are all doing fine
People offering up their time and skills
The type of caring and kindness that gives you chills

Don't get me wrong, these times are hard and new
I don't underestimate that, and neither should you
What I'm trying to say is have a little bit of hope
And while you're doing it don't forget to share the soap

One more final message to speak and share
If we all do our bit, I know we will get there
So, don't stop thinking of others, be safe and be kind
Make sure you look after your health and your mind

COVID-19 you've hit us all very hard
But we're altogether putting up our guard
Stand up strong, keep up the fight
Then this virus will once again be out of sight.

Jo Pullen

Stay Home!

"Stay home!" Boris said,
"It's easy to do,
Do a bit of gardening,
Play a game or two."

"Stay home!" Boris said,
"Take pressure off the NHS,
To help save lives,
Just go outside less."

"Stay home!" Boris said,
"It's important, it's a must
Only essential journeys
Avoid the train and bus."

"Stay home!" Boris said,
And the streets were silent,
And the schools did close,
To beat a virus unknown and violent.

"Stay home!" Boris said,
"We're not asking for your soul,
We just need a bit of help
Together we'll reach our goal."

"Stay home!" Boris said,
"It's the right thing to do,

It's inconvenient and boring,
But we'll all pull through."

"Stay home!" Boris said,
"It might be for a while,
But be positive, stay active
This will all be worthwhile."

"Stay home!" Boris said,
And the planes came to ground,
And in came the two-metre rule,
No toilet paper to be found.

"Stay home!" Boris said,
"The message is loud and clear,
Sit down on your sofa,
Don't show the Invisible Enemy fear."

"Stay home!" Boris said,
"To the key workers we give thanks,
They put their health on the line,
You just have to sit in your pants!"

"Stay home!" Boris said,
"Please think of others before you,
The elderly and the vulnerable
Whose health won't see them through."

"Stay home!" Boris said,
And lockdown became reality,

And social events were no more,
All to stop unnecessary fatalities.

"Stay home!" Boris said.

Lynsey E

Dad

The day the cemetery opened for visitors
Small relief embraced with desperate need,
Submerged in a tidal wave of melancholy,
Longing for a place to say goodbye to the ones lost,
The rows of graves that had since been filled,
All lambs to the slaughter of COVID,
Tears engulfed not just for my father but for all the victims,
I was not alone, surrounded by many families,
Over time, the blur of faces become familiar,
A man prays out loud with the melody of the Quran drifting,
The brother and sister who sit next to their relative's grave
on the bare ground, clutching ways to remain close,
The flowers increased day by as did numbers,
The incense scent would flow all the way to my side as I
stood over my father,
Unable to fathom that he was gone, just gone.
I felt the gaping hole.
My dad was one of thousands,
Precisely 48,000 as of yesterday.

Khan

United We Stand, Divided We Fall

As the world is witnessing a global crisis, we are feeling united and fragmented. First time in history, everyone has come together for resolving a single cause. This shows that we can overcome challenges together and support co-existence on the planet.

When the pandemic started, we didn't know how to cope up with the situation. The most interesting point is that we all had faith to figure out creative ways to deal with the situation.

Initially, it was quite challenging to adapt to new ways of thinking and behaving. I am fortunate to live with my family at this crucial time in life. We supported each other whenever it was getting tough to deal with isolation. I am happy to share ideas that we use to stay afloat.

Building the spirit of teamwork in the house. We all divided roles and responsibilities as the household chores increased a lot. We realised it's fun to work together and share responsibilities.

Playing sports, board games, going for walks together for lighter and fun moments.

Setting up a daily routine for housework, online schooling and office work. It gives all of us positive energy and purpose. We have started living in the present moment.

Reaching out virtually to our family, friends and neighbours to keep our bonds flourishing. Seeing opportunities in the challenges has been the biggest gift for our family.

We have to keep our hope and faith as we are all in this together.
Here are a couple of lines that describe our emotions in this pandemic -

Stand tall and strong amidst the storm,
Serve the nation in every situation
Be the guiding light in every moment,
Salute to everyone who is working tirelessly
Together we shall overcome
Be it day or night.

This crisis is a historical event and we want to look back with memories that helped us become better human beings who spread love, joy and peace on the planet.

Smriti Chandra

Rainbow

This is where it happened, just here where you are standing.
A shimmering airborne arch, a shower of shards, a landing.
The children found it first; came to colour their faces and fill their eyes
Turning this way and that peeping through the kaleidoscope's disguise.
This place was a magic glen, where sunbeams glittered and raindrops shone
Then the grown-ups came and the magic and the prism drops were gone.
They had heard the legendary tale of old
That buried on this spot was a crock of gold.
So they came with spikes and hammers, stones and axe blades
Levers, picks, some nitro and a clutch of spades.
They grimly chased each dancing, laughing child away;
And behind the cordon, began the business of the day.
The blows rained down and hacked into the crystal core
The sparkling colours fizzed and swizzled on the woodland floor.
The children watched in silence: they could only stand and stare:
To witness such destruction and devastation there.
The arc collapsed and shattered like a thousand window panes
They sifted through the diamond dew, but found no golden grains.

Men dug deep into the warm and yielding earth
And laid bare the radiant bud that gave the rainbow birth.
Here was the germinal, the source of indigo, orange and green
Budding tiny beadlets: of yellow, blue, red: secret and unseen.
They cared not for the miracle nor the magic of the light,
Each blamed his hapless neighbour, and they began to fight.
Undercover of confusion all the fairy folk came to set
And capture every vibrant shard in a tiny rain-droplet.
All around the droplets shimmered on the waves of grass
A million tiny rainbows, waiting for the sun to pass
And use its power to fuse them once more into an arc
with bands of brilliant colour, to rise above the park.

Sue Jones

An Ode To Anti-Bacterial Gel - Where Art Thou?

I've learned a new vocabulary
Since the virus came our way
I'm a microbiology expert
And I'm learning more each day.

Like hazmat suits and PPE
New phrases and terminology, too -
Such as 'squashing the peak of the sombrero'
I'm confused, a bit, are you?

My new modus operandi
Is all alone, just me
When going outside in public
Social distancing is the key.

I've said goodbye to football
Hair appointments - a thing of the past!
My fingernails are like talons
I wonder how long Shellac can last?

My history group is now history
My choir has folded too
My book club has hit the floor
I guess things are the same with you?

No more aerobics at the gym
No ladies' lunches, no supper club
It's a G&T in front of the telly
No more trips to the local pub!

No more 'Jam and Jerusalem'
Gone is the monthly WI
I try to laugh about it all
But really I could cry!

My mobile is my lifeline now
My old life is on hold
I've thrown away my diary
And I'm doing as I am told!

I'm organising wardrobes
My garden is like Kew!
My drawers can all shut tight again
But, there's so much more to do.

There are so many jigsaw puzzles to crack
And ageing neighbours to call for a natter
It's in unprecedented times like this
That we must hang on to what really matters.

Connecting with others in isolation
Is what we all must do
We will only get through this together
To one another we must stay true.

So let's beat this bloody virus
Send it packing, this COVID-19
Kill it with love and kindness
More than this world has ever seen.

Jan Vogel

Little Jack Frost

Now little Jack Frost he's the boss.
He'll get you on a winter's day no matter where you stray.

He creeps up behind and nips your feet and ruins the
farmer's wheat.
He'll even nip you when you sleep.

In the morning he'll still be there awaiting the early riser.
You don't have to be a bus driver, a milkman or a taxi driver.
He doesn't discriminate early or late.
He will be awaiting at the garden gate.

He'll catch your feet, your hands, your nose,
Even sheep and anything that grows.

You can see him on your breath.
He can cause you distress,
Slow your heartbeat and leave you in a mess.

Now Jack is fly, cunning and unique.
But one thing he does not like is the heat.
No matter what he does he cannot escape the burn of the
sun -
as this will ruin Jack's fun.

Albert McCall

Hominid-19

'Twas early last year, when the first positive case was identified. A virus was brought into hospital, infected with a strange, unidentified type of human. They now believe the human originated in a bacteria, and jumped species at a Wagamama's.

At first, Wagamama's tried to downplay the significance of this, but as more and more viruses became infected with humans, they were eventually forced to take drastic action, and quarantine every Wagamama's in the retail park.

Billions of viruses went on lockdown in their petri dishes, and with nothing else to do, Herd Inc., a popular videogame about a human-induced apocalypse, shot to the top of the charts.

The other restaurants still saw little threat from humans, with the likes of Nando's and Zizzi's laughing it off and making memes about it with Avengers Infinity War screenshots. Little did they know that humans were at that very moment, slowly making their way around the retail park via Deliveroo bikes and ice cream vans. Before they realised what hit them, viruses in KFC were struck down with humans, seemingly without any connection to Wagamama's!

All at once, doors throughout the Restaurant Group, once bastions of free movement of viruses, closed as eateries looked to their own. Across the pond on the high street, Arby's banned all travel from the Restaurant Group other than its own viruses coming home, but confused and contradictory advice meant that many viruses weren't screened for signs of human-infection upon arrival.

Retail park-wide shortages of napkins only exacerbated matters, and restaurant owners requested clothing manufacturers like Formula Onesie to switch production to napkins vital to protect viruses. We are now in the endless twilight of lockdown, and only time will tell if viruses can pull through, or be doomed by HOMINID-19...

William Robinson

Blue-Eyed Boy

You were the one for me,
Who knows what hold you had on me,
Like a spell I couldn't break free,
The smile when you looked at me,
Like a drug I couldn't break free,
Piercing blue eyes directly in mine.

You came to me and I succumbed to your spell,
Blue-eyed boy your spell hurts, please release me,
My heart on my sleeve, loosen the noose,
It's too late my sleeve has been caught,
I can't say no to you, I can't even grieve,
Let me leave, relieve the pain I feel.

I can't deal with how I felt with the cards I was delt,
Please blue-eyed boy set me free from this guilt and hate,
This situaton was it fate or bait?
Our own doing and no matter the decision,
Right or wrong but secrets are just a killer
Blue-eyed boy I told you everything,
Interested or not I will never know why was everything
complicated?

Head saying yes heart saying no, confusing mine,
Blue-eyed boy just tell me you love me,
Hoarding my thoughts, let me go,
Trapped trying to run free, my ego bruised,

Tell me blue-eyed boy, surrender your feelings, I'm so confused,
Forgive me, my heart's desire abused and used,

Blue-eyed boy I don't want to forget how it feels,
Without you blue-eyed boy your arms around me,
Your body on mine my first love let me forget,
Trust I see and I find in you every day for something new,
Blue-eyed boy my feelings for you,
It hurts too much, take them away for you and me too,

Blue-eyed boy you told me to leave,
My heart on the ground no longer on my sleeve,
You know I would have done anything for you,
Maybe it was what should have been done I believe,
Blue-eyed boy the spell of you I can never be freed.

Joshua Paul Fox

Confinement

I stare out of the window
Confined to these four walls
Our planet is in Limbo
The final curtain call?

I feel my heart still beating
With my hand upon my chest
I'm still here for a reason
While nature takes a rest

There is a silent enemy
But we're all aware
Just because it can't be seen
Doesn't mean it is not there

The days are rolling into one
And yet the world keeps turning
Our normal lives have come undone
The human race is learning

These times of great uncertainty
Have brought me great emotion
Like courage, strength, anxiety
Love and pure devotion

I need not look high for angels
As they're already here

Fighting on the front line
Facing all our fears

We will surpass the darkness
The light will shine again
The enemy is heartless
But our beating ones remain

I know that God is witnessing
The suffering endured
The time will soon be coming
When all illnesses are cured

So think not about money
Or material, man-made things
And you'll meet Mother Nature
See the wonders that she brings

When the rain goes
There are rainbows
After winter comes the spring
A time of new beginnings
And a chance to spread your wings

Although you may not see it
The world is not on hold
It just needs time to heal itself
Then beauty will unfold

We must stay strong
Unite as one
Each and every nation
Respect the air, the Earth, the sun
All of God's creation.

Hayley Edwards

The Final Commandment

Did God or Mother Nature have a hand in this?
Was it planned or simply hit or miss?
Was this a virus sent to hit us hard?

See millions dying and people crying
Can it really be that God could let this be?
But seeing birds once more and taking in the air and feeling
really free?

In times of isolation there is much introspection
I really thought this time I knew
That Jesus gave his life for millions and millions give their
lives to You.

Now in the small still hours
With the scents of new grown flowers
I sense that He did not walk in the garden alone.

Maybe this plan to save our fellow man
From wars and hate and tormented souls
Will let us grow and love as it is known.....

"For my last commandment was the easy one to do
Just to love one another
As I have loved you."

Meryn Williams

Victorious

COVID-19, why can't we see you? Were you a secret? Why do you have to destroy so many lives? Why can't we escape from you?

You have changed our world upside down. Why do you hurt us? Are you a stubborn and fierce virus?

Do you have a destination to go to? Where will you stop? What are you? I have many more questions about you.

Isolation, scared, loneliness, boredom, anger, destruction, destroy, trapped, fear, lies, scams, avoid, pity, mind games, manipulate are many negative words that are introduced into our lives.

Many people aren't resisting the urge to break the rules, Why? I do not understand.

NHS and key workers are fighting to save lives and risking their own, including the Prime Minister.

Do you deserve to die? Are we going through hell? Should we surrender? Want your freedom?

Then listen, we need to help others, do not be afraid, we can beat you COVID-19 and unite once again.

Show your compassion, kindness, enthusiasm, motivation, inspire others, have hope and courage.

It is not going to be easy, it'll be hard, mistakes will be made, it is alright to cry, we are human, we are allowed to feel and we can learn from this and others.

COVID-19, you will go to hell, we will beat you, it's simple, justice will be done.

We will honour all those loved ones lost forever.

NHS, key workers and everyone in this world, you are good-hearted people and are amazing, do not give up, keep going.
Everyone be a model to all children, lead the way, support and guide, do not threaten, punish or lecture.
Listen, honour, love and respect and soon darkness will disappear and we will be victorious.

Emma Broadwell

My COVID-19 Isolation Story

Six people young and old staying at home. Finding things to do, knitting, crochet, computer, phone, diamond art and the work around the house. Luckily we have quite a large garden and we got chalk and tried to play hopscotch on the drive. Some of us had trouble trying not to fall over. We have chickens and they often escape their fencing so we have to chase them around to stop them from going on the road. We do exercising with Mr Motivator on TV. We have drawn rainbows and put them and teddy bears in the windows, we stand at the windows every Thursday to clap and cheer all the key workers for their service, including NHS and private ambulance services, police, firefighters, dustmen, shopworkers, pharmacies and GPs.

We have two keyworkers who live in the south of England, Robert works as a supermarket supervisor and Stuart who is a full-time paramedic. We worry about them and miss them and their children and partners. We hope they stay as safe as they can and pray for this to be over.

We watch television but it is all repeats because not much filming can be done with the new social distancing laws. Getting shopping in is hard, trying to get a slot online then most things are out of stock because people have gone silly and stockpiled, then the dustmen complain because a lot of food is being thrown away as it has gone past its use by date. What a waste, so selfish when there are people out there who can't get enough food.

And what about the homeless, how do they cope? The government are putting up new hospitals why can't they do the same for the homeless? We all need to stand together and abide by the stay at home rule to beat this pandemic.

Sheila Marsh

Stay At Home

Many more families are going to lose loved ones,
he said.
These words stung my heart,
Like a wasp trying to protect itself,
This cannot be, I thought,
A virus - that's all
Just the flu?
No.
Many more families are going to lose loved ones,
he said.

It's everywhere now.
People are dying.
Fear coursing through our veins.
Britain closed.
Stay at home.
But how will I live?
How will I pay?
Will we all live to see another day?

We will give your businesses loans
80% of your pay
We will protect you
Yes,
Please, I pray.
This vicious virus - please stay away.

But you must stay at home,
Stay alone.
Socialism is great in a pandemic, always - I say.
We will protect you, but
Many more families are going to lose loved ones,
he said.

Stay home.
Protect the NHS.
Save lives.

That's what I'll do,
To avoid this global plague,
To stop it
From infecting my vulnerable lungs,
To protect each other
Save each other.

He's got it now,
And so many more
3000 deaths here,
And more worldwide
Please, let this plague subside.

Our superheroes,
Nurses
Doctors
Teachers
And more

Fighting for our lives,
Risking their own,
We salute you - I say.

When will this end?
Nobody knows.
So let's clap
Paint rainbows
Pray
Read and write
Be kind
And,
Do not roam.
Just stay at home.

Laura John

Powerful Drug

Remember this chapter when your history books write
We were all petrified as our hearts filled with fright
We argued, we reasoned, that we had the right
To just carry on and we'd all be alright

Reality dawned as the virus took hold
It had no compassion for the young or the old
Isolation was needed, this much we were told
Or else, like a card stack, the whole world would fold

And yet in this maelstrom, many heroes appeared
We stood in our doorways the NHS cheered
So many retirees were soon volunteered
It wasn't as bad as so many had feared

And when it's passed over

So tell someone you love them and give them a hug
We've all worked so hard to get rid of this bug
But let's learn a lesson and not be so smug
Belief in the future is a powerful drug.

Graham Hayden

Poem Of Peace

When the world is shut, and you are told that you must stay at home
Know that you might be within your own walls, but you are not alone
For each person is facing the same mysterious fight
Which is, how to battle the worry within your mind at night

When times are scary, and you feel as though this will put your mind to test
When there is madness everywhere you look, why not take this time to rest?
A few weeks of self-reflection, maybe figure out a new path
You can take a new turning in the aftermath

I'm aware of course that money does not grow on trees
Who would have thought, locked down from the fears of a sneeze
However it is what it is we can not change things with worry
I understand the kids are driving you mad, you wish bedtime would hurry

You feel as though you have lost all concept of time
I'm writing a poem again, words of peace with rhyme...

I'm looking out from my window just as confused as you
So let's just simplify things, and do what we are told to do

There will be ups and downs highs and lows
Grounded to a halt just like when it snows

I can not change things though, what will be will be
I will not give into fear through this uncertainty

So let's do things with honour, and act with integrity
If you are old or vulnerable, take that space in the line in front of me

Work together to prosper, unite at home, but work as a team
For this will be written about in history books,
The days of COVID-19.

Beth Abbott

Pandemic

When you wake up and think it's a dream
Reality hits and you want to scream
There's a deadly virus surrounding as all
We need to listen and be the ball
Listen to all of the advice that's being given
If you don't we will lose some of our living
For this short period in time
Please step up and stay in line
People are working all the hours and more
They can't go home and just shut their door
They are thinking of the horror they share
But they still do their job because they care
Stop being selfish and think what you do
Everyone is suffering and not only you
Please stay at home and be brave
Think of the people you may also save
So please just listen to what they all say
And maybe soon we will see light of day

Go home to family that live at your home
Stop over-shopping and having a moan
These precautions are put in place
So that we can save the human race
All the rules given you need to follow
The reality of this is hard to swallow
Protect yourself and your family too

But please where possible be selfless too
Play with your children and keep in touch
With the families and friends we love so much

This doesn't mean go out to the park
Or have parties and gatherings after dark
You can still speak to family or video call
To reassure them we are still standing tall
We haven't lost our bloody brains
Although I think many are insane
Going out thinking they know the best
And thinking of themselves and not the rest
We have a chance to make things right
So go home and hold loved ones tight
Lots of hope and love we should send and
Pray for this pandemic to come to an end.

Gemma Cullen

Self-Isolation

Time passes us by as our bodies run cold.
Good times a memory as our lives stand still.
We will survive this crisis but what does our future hold?
An invasion of life, such high numbers are ill.

Life is a roller coaster we scream but pull through.
Slowly moving up then crashing back down.
Through troubled times to ourselves let's stay true.
Studying wildlife to smile and not frown.

Birds are talking chirping and singing.
Grass is growing before our very eyes.
Are we looking ahead to what the world is bringing?
Or have we been punished for all the lies?

Families destroyed oh such a waste.
What did we do to deserve this life?
Without smell just fear and a lack of taste.
No family or friends, no hugging or strife.

I gaze from my window a boy with a kite.
To the sound in some gardens of children playing.
The warmth of the sun still shining bright.
Is it days, weeks or months we are staying.

But nature is with us colours alive
The sight of crimson, green, violet and blue.

Bees humming a tune return to their hive.
A squirrel catches my eye just me and you.

Oh, wonderful world where will this end.
Those special people risking their lives.
Whilst we study the cause is this a new trend.
For our children, parents husbands and wives

No more isolation please let me out.
I feel as though I'm a prisoner at home.
We are all suffering and can scream and shout.
But let us remember none of us are alone.

Robert Sarfaty

A Thing Called Love

For him and her -
forever would never be enough.

When she had too much
he picked her up
when she rolled over
his arm pulled her close.

When his hand crept into her pocket
fingers interlocked
when he squeezed her leg under the table
or ran his fingers up her thighs.

Movement embedded with lies.

When he kissed her forehead
just before bed
when he played with her hair
or they walked together,
in the sweet fresh air.

When he smiled at what she had to say,
when they laughed with one another
each and every day.
When he winked at her across the room
or they gazed upon constellations in the summery sky.

When she knew he was her best friend,
how was she supposed to know -
he would tear apart every inch of trust -
all for lust.

How was he supposed to know she'd come running back
due to her detrimental lack
of self-esteem.
How was she supposed to know where this would go
how was she ever supposed to know?

When he brushed her waist
and told her she was exquisite.
When he fooled her into thinking
she was more than just a visit.

When they were silent -
he looked into her eyes with nothing more to say
she didn't need to think it through,
not knowing what came next.

She thought quietly and to herself
I'm so completely, in love with you.

How was she ever supposed to know?

Molly Keating

Once More (A Child's Perspective)

When will friends come to play again?
And giggle as they knock on the door?
When will we go to school again?
And do normal things once more?

When can I hug my family again?
And laugh 'til we fall on the floor?
When can I go to the park again?
And do normal things once more?

When can we go on a train again?
And holiday by the shore?
When will we dance, swim and gym again?
And do normal things once more?

If all these things start to happen again,
There is something of which I am sure.
Life will be fresh and new again,
When we can do normal things once more!

As soon as the school bell rings again,
I'll be the first in line at the door.
I can't wait to sit at my table again
And do normal things once more!

When we can visit our family again,
I'll no longer moan and ask "What for?"
I can't wait to feel their warmth again
And do normal things once more!

As the markets and cafes re-open again,
I'll no longer call shopping a chore.
I can't wait to see all the people again
And do normal things once more!

When I can go on a plane again
I'll no longer find travelling a bore.
I can't wait to watch them soar again
And do normal things once more!

Maybe this is time to pause again?
And to evaluate humanity's flaws?
Will we appreciate life all over again?
When we can do normal things once more.

Rebecca Bennett

To The Parents

Hey everyone my name is Mal. I'm a single mum to ten awesome children who are all school age or college or left home.

Three different education settings, five different levels of learning and four with additional learning needs: autism, ADHD and personality disorder.

I would like to say to everyone that if me and my children can survive this then we all can. Single parents, we all know how this isolation can be lonely and scary, but most of all it's uncertain.

Life as we knew it will never be the same: shopping, activities, education settings.

Home-schooling is challenging enough but to lose out on GCSEs and SATs and end of year stuff for kids is terrifying to say the least. The point I'm trying to make is that though all this is happening, give yourselves a pat on the back, tell each other well done, you are not alone. We as a nation will go down in the history books as loving, caring and most of all brave and resilient to survive each day through this life-changing experience.

I think we all appreciate the level of care from our NHS, but also parents single or together we have done an amazing job of protecting our future generation.

So well done parents. Kids you are the most amazing human beings that we have the privilege of caring for.

To all the additional needs children and adults a huge well done for getting up each day and just coping with the uncertain world we now live in.
I would like to thank my children for the privilege of raising and caring for you, it's an honour.

Sarah James

Someone Cares

I felt that life had passed me by, no one cared if I should live or die,

It seemed to me that life was cold because I had no one to hold,

In deep despair I could have cried, I felt that I should run and hide,

What was the reason for me to live, I had so much that I could give,

And then a voice so sweet and low, a voice that I would come to know,

So reassuring and so kind, sounded in my troubled mind,

No one is ever truly alone, there's always someone there to hold,

Even if I can't be seen, or briefly in a passing dream,

I lie with you all through the night, around you my arms I clasp so tight,

I walk beside you in the day, and I can hear everything you say,

I guide you gently by the hand, when sometimes you don't understand,

Comfort you when you feel down, close your eyes I can be found,

The lightest touch, the softest sigh, it's me, I'm here, so don't you cry,

No one truly walks alone, on wings of love I bring you home,

A guardian angel there to care, so smile and try not to despair,

If no one seems to give a damn, you always know just where
I am.
My gentle wings will you enfold, my arms so ready for you to
hold,
You're precious to me in every way, I'll never leave, I'll
always stay,
And if its time for you to leave, I`ll walk with you and gently
lead,
So now you know that someone cares, you have a love we
both can share,
And even when you find another, I'll love you both just like a
mother.

Judith Pearson-Garbutt

The Emerald

The eye of a tiger glowing green mist,
Part of ring finger waits in tight fist.

A sign of power that knows its own way,
Emerald flower demanding: obey!

I know its commends, I fear it all.
I do see its strengths, but I play it small.

Why do you all choose to play your life small?
That's nothing to lose by accepting it all!

The Goddess queried, the question is kind.
Will I be freed from my prison of mind?

The emerald sparks inviting to life
A living from heart, the true body's wife.

'Cause when it connects to truth in the heart,
No lies, wars or pests can harm body's art.

We are just like kids neglecting own toys,
The true body needs are shunned by mad boys.

Is not our heart, but only the greed,
Is not true love's cart, but fears that lead.

The green light wands, they travel from heart,
Arrive in the hands: the pure healing art.

Accept it all now, are gifts from the gods,
Make mind take a bow to the divine floods.

Then all falls in place: heart, body and mind,
Then God shows its face to you and your kind.

The heart voice can reign, the mind will comply,
Body with no pain, its youth will apply.

It's all in the heart, a new love of self,
Do learn its pure part in finding yourself.

Anna Grace

The Good Not Hood

This might sound out of the ordinary
But regardless of what society does, says and feels about
me
I try to still see the good not hood in them
Everyone has a negative *aspect* to them
Which I won't elaborate on
But some of these entities can be so strong
It causes society problems
It's like their presence has taken over the whole universe
Leaving the good, not hood, in worms
Fighting for their lives in the earth
Words can't describe that this is the mirror reflection of me
So precise, but I do have my flaws
Scared to death, I can't walk free
Just to be gnawed
It's not that I'm the good not hood type of character
This is my self-painted portrait
Nobody else has painted that picture
If they used their brain they could see how one's maintained
I'm not God's gift to Earth
I'm God's creation to nurse the dying from falling
I don't want to be placed on a hearse
Knowing when I was alive I treated society like dirt
That's what they've been doing to me in reverse
Splashing contempt, making me exempt
It's not just the potential I have

But for more world peace I'm wishing for
Please don't forget that I raised my hand
That I have something creative in store
And that's in my glands.

Natalie Peterson

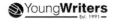

NHS

The NHS supplies the healthcare
That we could ever need,
With treatment free wherever
That's the promise yes indeed

That ambulance when you call it
The doctor who's on call,
Even in the middle of the night
You will no doubt get it all

The A&E departments
Perform a very special task,
To stitch us back together
Just when and where we ask

They cope with all the traumas
Which they experience every day,
And if you really need their help
They won't send you away

We all criticise its failings
When the management isn't right,
But let's not forget the work they do
In the middle of the night

The accident from the roadside
The child that may be sick,

These people have to deal with those
They cannot choose and pick

We should praise doctors and nurses,
For this dedication that they show,
Who knows when it will be our turn
That we never ever know

We hope it does not happen
That it's them we need to call,
For ourselves or for our loved ones
Perhaps they have only had a fall

Just hope it's not more serious
When your health is not intact,
Be sure that's when you need them most
That is certainly a fact.

James Ackland

When This Is All Over...

When this is all over, we'll go back to what we knew
The children's school run
The drive to work
And a trip to Starbucks at two.

When this is all over, we'll go back to what we liked to do
Friday drinks at Tiffany's
BBQs in the sun
And a trip to the seaside to dip our toes in the sea for fun.

When this is all over, we'll see the people we love
Grandma and Grandpa who live just down the road
To chat and joke with our friends
And to reunite with our mates at work who have all been working from home.

When this is all over, we'll be able to make a plan
The next upcoming festival
A trip to London town
And a plane ticket to anywhere to feel excited in the air.

When this is all over, when, we do not know
We must be grateful for what we have
And to appreciate life as we do.

When this is all over, we would have come together as one
Be thankful for our NHS
For their sacrifices and love

When this is all over, as a nation we will stand
We know it couldn't have been easy,
But thank you Boris you're a pretty top man.

But this is not over yet
We have a long way to go
You know the drill, you're doing great
Just stay home!

Samantha Martin

Coronavirus

Coronavirus,
What can I say,
I wish you would just go away.
Invading the world
And roaming about,
Now no one is allowed to go out.
We can only go out to get exercise
For an hour a day,
And everybody must stay two metres away.
Schools are shut,
Certain shops too,
Can't go anywhere unless it's essential to you.
People wearing masks
And panic buying,
Across the country people dying.
In a hospital bed,
All alone on their own,
Because they can't have any visitors or go home.
We can't go to the park
Or on vacation,
At the moment there is no vaccination.
No visiting friends
Or drinks in the pub,
No visiting family or the ones that we love.
Key workers daily,

Risking their lives,
While pleading with us to be safe and stay inside.
Singing Happy Birthday,
While washing our hands,
Standing on doorsteps clapping for NHS staff all across our land.
Everybody waiting,
For the day,
When Boris comes on TV to say.
Well done everybody, lockdown is done,
Coronavirus is gone, we did it, we won.

Natalie Tansey Corbett

Soon

When quarantine is over,
I will paint my eyelids yellow
And my bitten-down nails will match;
Model new clothes from a birthday I celebrated
On Skype 'til three.
And curl my hair,
Four inches shorter than it was,
A startling cherry red.

I'll drop a tub of mango sorbet
At a friend's house;
She has a degree to finish.
Education comes first,
School's not out, yet.

I'll break in new shoes,
And play ding dong ditch at my best friend's house,
Tackle her in an embrace.
She'll be dressed up too.
We'll jump in her car,
Roll the windows down and sing in traffic,
Speeding straight ahead.

Buy lunch at a service station,
Sunbathe on the hood of her car;
Hands sticky with ice cream.
We'll put on our sunglasses for the first time,

And continue along our country's tarmac veins
To visit somewhere new.

When quarantine is over,
We'll kick-start a summer we've been craving,
And make up for lost time.

We made it;
We'll make sure we live.

Imogen Smiley

We Will Get Through This

We live in strange and uncertain times.
We feel scared, for our
Family and friends and loved ones.
Schools shutting, jobs becoming unsure as this virus takes hold.

We can't hug or see are older family members or those who are at risk,
as they are at a greater risk as this virus unfolds.
Take each day as it comes and try not to panic
though you may want to as I do.
We can and will get through this, it will not beat us.

When this is finally over we can all hug the people we are close to
our friends and family
Like we have never hugged them before and
Not take it for granted.

We can go out and see our friends and family and loved ones.
We can see nature at it's best. We can enjoy the company of others again.

For now it is hard for everyone, the young, the old, the people and friends we love.
Take time to stop and to think and say to yourself we will get to the other side.

Though times are dark just now, there is always
A little bit of hope, we just have to hang onto it and see the light through the darkness.

Sarah Langridge

At Home In Lockdown

Longer days,
warmer weather,
allowed one walk.
Trees are near to leaf;
blossom sprinkles,
here and there.
We enjoy still
spring fare.

It is an episode,
but nature follows
season's path.
Our lives need
to find resource,
in appreciation
for home activities,
that once we left,
when outside
and rushed to work -
school all busy, busy.

Now, to listen, not just talk;
with family members,
who were in our lives;
but more in passing,

than understanding
and appreciating.

To talk on phone;
give FaceTime
or maybe Zoom
to meet a group,
that we were part,
before locked out.

To make routine,
in daily round that
secures each day,
yet gives time,
for interests shared.

Appreciation for
those who bravely work,
in hospitals, supermarkets,
and everywhere to keep,
that lifeblood tick of care.
Provision for all of us,
now at home to
slow, stall and finally
end pandemic.

Colin Coles

A Cat Poem

Mouse.....our Feline Friend

Black and white,
big green eyes that talked to us
contented, fearful, pleading, blinking, staring,
all-seeing.

Our feline faithful friend.
Always there to greet us
coming to meet us, tail aloft.

Our feline furry friend.
Thick fur, daily cleaned
by a rasping tongue.

Our feline fussy friend.
Always there at mealtimes
ready to try new foods,
Tuna, prawns, mince, liver (his favourite) pilchards,
a look of disdain when offerings
were not to his taste!

Our feline fearless friend.
Patrolling his territory, repelling the enemy,
tooth and claw.
Bravely curious and inquisitive.

Our feline fearful friend.
Ready to run,
ready to hide,
ready to retreat when the doorbell rang.

Our feline faithful, furry, fussy, fearless, fearful, fluffy friend.
Warm, comforting trusting, loveable, demanding, intelligent.
Curled up on my lap sleeping.
Mouse, our feline friend.

Linda Drywood

True Blue Heroes

She dons the gown of pleasing blue
And comfortable shoes of white
Then she prepares her sterile attire
For the pressures of the night

He dons the mask and gloves of blue
And an apron of purest white
Encumbered is he in anxious ire
A soldier before the fight

They wear their shields with steely pride
Resolve set in every heart
Duty calls at every turn
For each end there is a start

Days and nights that last so long
Waiting for a time to sleep
And rest and eat beyond the fatigue
When all you can do is weep

Where care is equal to everyone
Despite their circumstance of birth
Unlocked from Heaven to help us
Those vital angels on Earth

Who will win this battle's run
In this age of plastic armour?

Where microscopic foe persists
In this global panorama

True blue heroes one and all
Fight for life in the face of death
This new enemy they must defeat
For the sake of our national health.

Margaret Edge

Coronavirus

The Coronavirus or COVID-19
Has swept the world over
Young people, elderly
It gives no quarter
People are dying
The sadness is rife
But there is hope for us all
Take the government's advice
Stay at home, keep safe
Don't venture outside
There are things we can do
Each day if we try
Phone an old friend
You haven't seen for a while
You can have a laugh
Reminisce for a while
It will make you feel good
For quite a time
Phone up a neighbour
Who lives all alone
It will make them feel better
Hearing you on the phone
Wave from your window
Smile
You will get one back

Just write things down
Of a memory you have
Like a good shopping trip
Where you had such a laugh
Take out old photos
You haven't seen for a while
You can picture those days
Sure to bring on a smile
It will pass the days pleasantly
You can do it anytime
Will bring out the sunshine
And a lovely blue sky.

Jeanette Gaffney

They Say...

They say to stay inside
and only go out once for exercise

They say to work from home
and to educate our own

They say to clap at 8pm every Thurs from now on
to give thanks to the NHS staff for being so strong

They say to grocery shop in a considerate and infrequent manner
to allow others to buy food and not miss out on nutritious matter

They say to paint rainbows and place teddy bears in our windows
so that we can still feel connected and not like earth widows

They say a lot of things... to make us feel that we are in control,
they are in control

But we're not, not really... how have we got here?

How have we ended up only beginning to think of others,
reaching out and taking responsibility for our own actions now?
When we are on a cliff edge of humanity as we know it.

They say... things will never be the same again.
Good I say, because what we had become was hideous.

Serena B Robins

With An Eye On The Sky

So I turned the corner
Following the map you made and sent to me
On neatly rolled brown paper
With lines, contours and colours
At the bottom a guide

I went from concrete to trampled down earth
The passing of cars turned to wind in the many trees
The description you wrote leading me into the wild
And of course I started to sneeze
My eyes to leak

The lines of the contours lead me up and up
My feet climb on strong but my lungs are sore
The sun is so brilliant and the final destination
Is not so far now
On I push up and up

I'm at the top now taking a breath
Some well-received water
When I spot a little cairn
I investigate it and on it lay my hands
To find a little note with a last instruction

I lay myself down
On the soft grass
With a picture of you
And imagining you
With an eye on the sky.

Andy Bunn

Light Overcomes Dark

These times are so uncertain,
We don't know which way to turn,
Not allowed to come or go,
And parents are each taking turn
One doing the shopping
And the other stuck at home,
Teaching the kids geography
And now onto English lit
And all Mummy wants to do
Is get a chance to sit!
The kids want to go outside
And play with everyone
But we can't forget the reason why,
We all stand as one.
We have to follow protocol
We have to play by the rules
For we're all in this together
We've been given all the tools.
Our doctors, nurses, paramedics,
All fighting the frontline
Against this invisible enemy
They will defeat in time.
But for now we all need
To play all our parts
And don't forget to love everyone

Keep them in your heart.
As this won't last forever
Light will overcome
Dark.

Bridget McGinty

Ummi's Perfume

My soul smiles,
As I inhale
The sweet smell
Of my mother, my ummi.

The comfort and warmth
Of her fragrance
Makes me feel safe
Against the world's race.

As she moves around the room
Her aroma lingers in the air
Oh how I long to be with her,
Every day throughout the year.

As she softly strokes my hair
I close my eyes and thank my Lord
For giving me the blessings of my mother
My cushion, every time I fall.

I sit miles away
Reminiscing the times we spent together,
Each day implementing her behaviour
Gentle, strong, patient and sincere.

Oh how I long to be with her
As I sit far away,

Remembering her smile
I start my day.

Even though she is not by my side
My soul still smiles
As I stop and remember,
The comfort of her aroma and her charming charisma.

Aisha Iqbal

COVID-19

In our bid to outwit the COVID-19
We're told to self-isolate.
In the weirdest way we've ever seen
We await our terrible fate.

I'm stuck inside for most of the day
Checking each cough and sneeze,
Feeling my brow every possible way
Listening for every wheeze.

At every chance I check the mirror
For signs of impending doom,
At the slightest glimpse of any pallor
I'm locked in terrible gloom.

I take my pulse as the clock ticks by
O how the heart does race!
Scared half to death and don't know why
But it's only the sight of my face.

O grave where is thy vistory
O death where is thy sting?
Isolation is mandatory
To escape this virus thing.

So I'll fill my time with telly and tea
And biscuits from the tin
And die instead of obesity
So Corona will not win.

Fiona Martin

War With A Virus

The world has gone silent
A regression in time
Alone yet together
A motive-free crime

Normality a memory
Routine never more
The play is exciting
But the script is a bore

Nothing feels right
It seems so unfair
The shops are now closed
The streets are all bare

No laughter is heard
From a zoo or a park
No splashing in pools
Or films in the dark

But what is our fear
And why do we hide
In our makeshift prison
Without friends by our side

Why can't we travel?
Why aren't we free?

Was it something we did
Should we blame you or me?

Blame's not the answer
We must find a cure
And until we do
Stay behind your closed door

For alone as we feel
Together we'll unite
To win this cruel battle
With an isolated fight.

Abbie Khangaroot

Lockdown 2020

We've got rainbows in our windows
And teddy bears there too
So children on their daily walks
Have something nice to do.

On Thursdays the United Kingdom
Really does unite
As we stand out on our doorsteps
To clap the heroes of this fight.

Our homes are now our fortress
Isolation is our moat
Each one of us must do our bit
We're all in the same boat.

Separated from our loved ones
We must stay safe inside
And honour all the key workers
That fill our hearts with pride.

There will be thousands who do not make it
Their loss will make us cry
The hardest thing for those left behind
Was that they couldn't say goodbye.

One day this will be over
And when this world nightmare ends
We'll treasure the small things in life
And the importance of family and friends.

Heather Dinnage

Did You Appreciate?

Did you appreciate your mate?
They came on short notice,
For you to cry on in a state.

Did you appreciate your partner on a date?
You went to the local cinema,
Even though the film wasn't that great.

Did you appreciate staying at the office late?
You got all that work done,
And you got home at eight.

Did you appreciate that chat at your garden gate?
With your friendly neighbour,
When no two metre distance could dictate.

Did you appreciate a family debate?
When you gathered for a big party,
And to celebrate.

Did you appreciate the gym to lose weight?
Going where you pleased,
No worries on your plate?

Now we appreciate, but we don't know the world's fate,
We must stay together, from afar,
Spreading love and not hate.

Delphi McWilliam

Often Mistaken

We as a society
Are always wanting,
Always needing.
Never being entirely satisfied.
From the latest technology to our relationships.

We are always craving more.
Never happy with what we have.
Forever curious if the grass really is greener on the other
side.
But I think in times or crisis.
We learn how to value the everyday.
To value the unimportant.

From the food on our shelves that we just take,
To the freedom we have to live the lives we have always
dreamt of.
To experience every form of human emotion,
and share our beautiful raw experiences with one another.

Now that we sit back and we reflect.
On our freedom,
Our wealth.
We begin to appreciate the true luck we have been granted,
And appreciate this luxury,
We often mistake for ordinary.

Rebecca Coppell

Thoughts On The Chelsea Flower Show 2005

We can't all get to Chelsea
Or to the gardens at Kew
For reasons such as distance and work hours,
And hayfever, to name but a few.

So we have to look elsewhere for our pleasures
If we want to see something new,
On our way to work or down to the shops
To get a different view.

There are buttercups down in the corner,
The sky is a lovely blue;
Birds are singing in the treetops
With sounds of twittering and the occasional coo.

The neighbours have croci and tulips,
And wildflowers of every hue
Abound in the hedges and waste ground
For butterflies to flutter through.

It would be nice to go to Chelsea
Or visit the gardens at Kew;
But there's really no need, as the Aborigines plead,
By naming a wood "Look Around You".

Kathy Rawstron

Memory Lane

Memory lane unveiled itself,
revealing a never-ending path,
surrounded by woodland and mountains.

The what-ifs from moments we didn't take,
rippled through the tops of the trees.
Echoing whispered temptations
of times that had long passed.

Brightly decorated houses marred the streets,
protecting dusty possessions
of passions once loved,
and dreams once shared.

Hundreds of people passed through Memory Lane,
leaving footprints as their lives once intertwined.
Some remained ingrained forever,
others a fading imprint.

There was never a definitive smell.
Sometimes my favourite meal would waft through,
other times your favourite brew.

What if Memory Lane was a real place?
Would you explore nooks and crannies with me?

Emma Berry

Birds In A Cage

Cooped up birds in a cage; chirping,
as far as the eyes could see:
hundreds of acres of land.

They breathed in the crisp air,
it made them bang their heads
against the chicken-wired coated cage.

Heads prickled in a menacing trap,
paused at the edge of the cage,
eyes startled but moved violently.

Wings felt tired from its lack of use,
or maybe its over-use, forced to
rest until the lock *unlocks.*

They looked at each other
waiting to hear a cruel cackle -
no sound was heard.

Little feet hit the ground and lift to
wings soaring once again across
the clear blue skies in the crisp air.

What once was never came back:
pollution had decreased and the birds
could see and breathe a little easier.

Hosany

Silver Linings

So here we are sitting at home in what they call lockdown,
We're allowed out once a day for a walk around town.
The streets are empty, the schools are closed and the supermarkets raided,
Our dreams of summer holidays and seaside visits faded.
But it's not all doom and gloom there are good things about this,
Parents are witnessing children doing things they might well otherwise miss.
The air pollution has dropped and the animals are thriving,
The roads are quiet and there is no noise because nobody is driving.
We do miss family and friends that I can't deny,
But when else will we get the chance to take stock and watch the world go by.
We should just try and make light of this strange situation,
Without the daily hustle and grind we can ignite our imagination.

Nina West

Immanuel

I cannot place this feeling that grows within my soul.
It is the strangest of fears,
perhaps of this unknown.
Am I in mourning?
For this feeling resembles loss...
All are well that are dear to me,
and yet their faces I can no longer see.
No, we must all stay apart,
although missing you all tears at my heart,
but better days are yet to come,
and we will all be together when this war has been won.
So for now let the flame of hope burn bright in you,
for the Lord our God brings life anew,
and even in the deepest of sorrows,
He brings us the promise of tomorrow.
Put your hand in the hand of the man that walked on the
water, for he will bring you strength.
Our Father walks beside us,
on him we can depend.
There is but one redeemer,
the cornerstone of life,
and believe me he is with us through all our fears and strife.

Eileen Louise Walls

Slowing Down

The morning rush was such a fuss
To get all fed and on the bus
To work, to school or to the gym
Keeping us busy, taught and trim

But now the days just stretch ahead
And no one needs to leap from bed
The pressure's off to see the boss
Maybe I'll make some applesauce

I'm taking time to go offline
And tune into this new springtime
It's quieter now and the air is clear.
If you stop awhile the birds you'll hear.

We've all slowed down
Don't rush to town
In traffic jams
That made us frown

We take our time and stand in line
We're grateful to those in the frontline
We'll pass this time and be just fine
And look forward to summer in the sunshine.

Amanda Donohoe

Our World In Progress

The world is fighting hard to heal,
People are focusing on families and food.
It also matters a lot about how we feel,
So we turn to music and hobbies to lift up our mood.

Each day feels like survival of the fittest,
No one could have prepared for the tragedy we're facing.
The clock ticks slowly each day but we're here as a witness,
To positive results and hope for history in the making.

A change will come, as life will begin if we manage to just
stay strong.
Fight for hope, fight real hard, soon everything wrong will
come undone.

Here's to us, here's to the world, we really are trying our
best.

We'll be stubborn and we'll be safe, after all, this is just
God's big test.

Zaibah Cossar Iqbal

New Life

Haiku poetry

You met your grandson
For the first time yesterday
Through a windowpane

Him: pink-faced, newborn
You: wrinkles creasing in joy
Divided by glass

Palms pressed against glass
A tiny clenched fist raised up
Unable to touch

But better to miss
This first hug he won't recall
Than all those to come.

Jenni Harrison

Spread The Love

When the sun comes up
It's time to bake
Bake some cake but don't leave it in too late
Family time is key
Making memories everyone can see
Take some pictures
Share with family
Save to gallery til things get happy
Treasure the times we spend together
Life's too short to cry together
Be kind and positive
Make times imaginative
Stay strong and unite
Even though at times you don't feel like
Spread the love
Like wings of a dove
Play games and paint
And learn to decorate
Watch films and cuddle
And get everything in a muddle
Be strong be calm
As we have got this in our palm
Don't give up on hope
This world will cope
Spread the love.

Cody Hayman

Feel Our Pain

Our eyes look to the floor, our spirits too,
No hope in sight, what shall we do?
The leaders say do this do that,
How do they know what they say is right for us?
They're in their big houses making decisions like these,
They have hundreds of thousands sitting in the bank,
And people like me don't have 1p,
Why don't they try living like us,
They wouldn't survive let alone getting on a bus,
This pandemic is real and so are we,
Teaching my four kids at home with no money,
I'm self-employed and now I can not work,
No help for me or my family,
We hope we survive through this pain and struggle,
If the Corona doesn't get us, not having any money will.

Katherine Fitzgerald

Not Isolated But Loved

Today I enjoyed being home
The place where no one is alone

Today I discover that I am strong
The strength that I got from being home

I know I am saving so many lives
not working front line but staying away from not touching
anyone

I know it's not easy to stay indoors
But you need to remind yourself that you are not alone.

If we unite and fight and come together
We can reach to the mission with all the possible measures

I'm loved and cared by everyone in the house
That's why it's not isolation it's being healthy and sound.

Share the love and keep your distance
This is the time to explore your existence.

Afreen Fatima

Isolation Plus

I've never been more thankful
For the wondrous works of Disney
Filling time with song and rhyme
For my little girl as well as me

It calms me down most when I think of yet more toast
Or is it cereal, to use the milk today?
How much coffee is too much
And how much electric have we used did you say?

So shall we find Nemo or Dory
Or a good musical so we can sing?
I could probably watch Frozen again
Maybe let's be creative and make something

If only I had some ingredients or equipment
And my little girl had the same attention span
So this afternoon I'll dive back into a feature
After all, I am a huge Disney fan.

Sarah Waterhouse

The Song Of Summer

Birds twittering in the summer air,
Rich green leaves on trees once bare.

Bees buzzing busily for endless hours.
Brushing pollen from the flowers.

The taste of summer on one's tongue.
The scent from nectar, sweet and young.

Fresh new eyes see fruits from spring.
Birds' song, new life makes hearts sing!

Our senses crisp with renewed pleasure.
These are delights we cannot measure.

Summer rain, soft to the earth.
Refreshes colours and thoughts of mirth.

Stars appear in clear night skies.
Nature heals the saddest eyes.

Our wealth we're sometimes apt to miss.
In this world man's so remiss.

Monica Buxton

COVID-19

A virus fast approaching we barely understand,
Taking lives of loved ones and destroying our plans.

A punishment it would seem, but what did we do?
A comeuppance maybe, that was long overdue?

No matter the reason for this troublesome time,
We can all help each other face the mountain we'll climb.

Change is inevitable and things will be tough
But family stick together through the good and the rough.

When it all gets too much and you think you're alone,
Don't be afraid to pick up the phone.

We may not endure the same worries as you,
But with love and support we will all make it through.

Amie Swarbrick

Lockdown

Oh my goodness! what a year,
2020 we live in fear.
Shop shelves empty, what a fast,
Everyone panic buying as if it's the last.
There's plenty, share it out,
think of those that can't get about.
We have been told to stay at home,
So why do some feel they should roam?
Listen carefully to the request,
Everyone else is doing their best.
We all miss our families and our friends,
Do as you're told and there will be an end.
A big thank you to all, stay safe, keep well,
We will have a big party and ring all the bells.
We need to stand together and unite,
Pull through together, with a fight.

Tina Claxton

Lockdown

Lockdown for twelve weeks
No strangers to be seen
A house usually kept pristine
Now looks lived in and not very clean
Parents now at home full time
Children being taught online
Making meals from packets and tins
And many other edible things
Kids wanting attention from morning to night
The electricity bill going sky high
Recycling bins left empty and bare
Kids using the bits to make art with flare
Painted pasta necklaces hanging about
Colourful rainbows fill windows throughout
Peace and quiet is a thing of the past
Meaningful conversation is ripe at last
For me the lockdown wasn't full of worry and stress
It was spent with my children and was totally the best.

Daniel Stoddern

Be Safe

It waits for you at the supermarket
It follows you to the pub
It covers the door handles we turn and the buttons we press
It doesn't care about age or race
It is all around you and it stares you straight in the face
It likes your friends and family
Especially when you hug
It hides in plain sight, an invisible killer bug
Wash your hands to zap its strength
Stay at home so it can't breed
Protect the ones you love by denying it its need.
So listen. Don't be stupid or think *it won't get me*
You could have that on your gravestone.
Just think how that would be...

Lee Cartwright

Stay Safe Daddy!

S uch long days are without you

T o run and play, only with mummy.

A re you thinking about us?

Y et, we miss you every day.

S tay safe Daddy!

A nother day of delivering parcels has come.

F etch us some treats on your way back home,

E aster eggs, chocolate, does not matter, as long as it is sweet.

D awn is approaching,

A re you safe out there my beloved husband,

D id you get something to eat throughout the day?

D elivery driver, husband, and daddy

Y ou are our hero, you keep us all safe...

Elina, Elizabeth and Elize Snepste

School Staff

In the future, when life returns to normality, what will happen on Thursday evenings at 8pm.

Probably people will be commuting home.
Eating dinner
Homework
Bath time and bed
Storytime,
Popping to the gym
Watching TV
Etc, etc.

If anything comes out of this current crisis, wouldn't it be lovely if
we gave a thought to everyone who's keeping life moving every day of the year.
Just once a week.
Low paid people who are now national heroes and always will be.
Wherever I am on Thursday at 8pm, heroes will always be in my heart
How about you!

Wendy Bannister

Coronavirus

We're all in this together
In our world right through
But nothing lasts forever
There's hope for me and you
Even in our darkest days
When the months ahead look bleak
I know that we will find a way
With that vaccine that we seek
Patience is the only thing
Needed by everyone
And then we can begin
To let our lives go on
From all the front line heroes
And key workers too
You all deserve a medal
For the hard work you do
With the sacrifices made
With very little fuss
We will find a way
To conquer this virus.

Brenda McDonald

Family

Hello, my good families, I bring love and patience to endure this time of COVID-19. As a family we've been at home for quite some time now, knowing already it is not easy for all of us. Try to be patient and love more your family with love of God. We all will be saved. The love of God is the foundation of our present condition.

So remember with God's love we can trust our wisdom, our creativity and our capacity.

In conclusion I think only love will help us but if we don't love ourselves we could never make it. Only be faithful in everything you do, I think is the answer for us.

Blessing Chinazor

Stay Strong

Coranavirus can do a lot of things to us, but it can't:
Stop us loving our family and friends
Stop the world from turning
Stop the sun from shining
Stop the flowers from growing
Stop the birds from singing
Stop the tides from ebbing and flowing
Stop day following night
Stop the clouds from forming in the sky
Stop the dawn from breaking
Stop the stars from twinkling
Don't despair, stay strong, the storm will pass
And, in the meantime,
Cherish and enjoy all those things that we have
Which will never change.

Mike Perry

Front Line

All hail the heroes of the front line,
The ones holding society's book together by the spine.
The doctors and the nurses,
Working flat out until this thing reverses.

All hail the heroes of the front line,
The ones holding society's book through strength combined.
The supermarket workers and delivery drivers,
Risking themselves until we all become survivors.

All hail the brave key workers -
Without you, this time would be far darker.
So have our gratitude for your unity
And undying toil for our community.

Zabou Claoue de Gohr

Carers And NHS

C lap for the carers!
A lthough times are tough they are there for us
R emaining strong, they carry on
E very day they take good care
R unning every morning just to catch the bus
S ame as us they still breathe air

A ll around the world, they stay united
N ever giving up hope
D elivering their services to those who can't cope

N ational Health Service, our heroes
H elping those in need, but not out of greed
S aving the day, once again.

Jeanelle James

Not Alone

Darkness surrounded me like a heavy blanket,
I tried to shake it off, tried hard to get rid of it.
It would not move, it would not budge,
I wanted someone to give it a nudge.
No matter how I twisted, no matter how I squirmed,
The heaviness remained, it seemed here to stay,
It was as if I didn't have a say.
Then suddenly an oh so tiny speck of light,
Burst through the darkness with all its might.
Bit by bit more specks appeared
They filled my world and brought me cheer.
And then I knew that He was there.

Sandra Changa

With You I Stare

Although it seems the world is down,
I sit with you and we can't help to see what's around.
We're lucky we have life and health,
With you I stare we don't need no wealth.

The days pass we need to keep strong,
I know it's hard to explain what's wrong.
I'm glad we have love and power,
With you I stare at every hour.

We can do this just keep going on,
All the fears of never knowing.
Every breath we can get through this together,
With you I stare always and forever.

Melissa Ward

Limz Military Collection

Sometimes you can have a bad day,
sometimes it seems that those days will not go away, but
keep your heads high and keep strong and work as one.

Just like the military does when a task needs to be
completed.

Don't be afraid to be yourself
because you are important just like any other queen or king,
so if you are having a bad day, just remember it will not last
forever and don't forget to keep your heads high.

Keep strong and work as one.

Just like military does when a task needs to be done.

Military Limz

Light At Tunnel's End

At times like this it's hard to see the light at tunnel's end
but please know this, though we've not met
you are a treasured friend.
Young or old, rich or poor
these things they matter not
for what really unites us are not the material things we've got.
What matters is we're human
What matters is we care
What matters is, whatever we have that we are prepared to share.
Don't feel sad, you must stay safe
This madness will be over.
And then, I promise, you can all come over.

Samantha Scarr

Stay Safe

Tossing, turning in my bed
Strange thoughts running through my head
Who, what, where and why
Making people worry and cry
Try not to feel so blue
No one else has any clue
Virus, virus everywhere
Does anyone even care?
Lockdown is being done
Come on everyone, it's not fun
We can do this and be united
Don't go out... stay isolated
A few weeks, it's not so bad
Maybe it'll save somebody's dad
Come on, let's say it loud
Stay home, stay safe and be proud.

Ayshea Hanif

Grandma's Tin

A vintage tin
brim-full of buttons
like atoms, packed inside matter.
Give it a shake, hear them
dozens of hostages tapping the walls.
Lift off the lid, release them
odd sizes and colours
bursting everywhere
forming galaxies on the carpet
Red Giants, White Dwarfs.

Capture them
pellet them into the tin.
Some have travelled
the furthest reaches of the room.
Shoot under grandpa's chair
to recover the minutest ones.
Resist the urge
to eat some of them.

Jodi Green

Thank You NHS

An army in health and safety dress
Very special people
With something quite rare
What makes you special people?
Is simply that you care
By ambulance or walk-in wounded
Everyone is treated, no one is excluded
While the labs are searching
For a virus cure
Your attention to duty is steadfast and pure
When we are done with COVID-19
And no longer need masks and screens
There should proper be redress
And we should do more than say
Thank you NHS.

Kevin Cottham

To Grandma From Grandad

Do you remember me?
I don't remember your name
But I feel I recognise your face

I once had a family
And it was marvellous
But they left without a trace

I had a mother
I had a father
And a wife I love more than ever

We had three lovely children
Then the children had children
Which brought our family together

She sometimes called me a silly old man
I never understood why
But I love her still
With all my heart
Until the end of time.

Claire Jones

Ponder

As we sit and wait,
As a nation in isolation,
It gives us time to think,
Reflect Mother Nature to reset,
Humanity in lockdown,
Wild animals roam free through locked windows our eyes can see.
But soon this virus will be stopped in its track,
And our freedom,
Normality will duly be back.
But for now we sit back and can only observe whilst the statistical graph
Takes a better curve,
Time spent with loved ones,
Friends far away,
Until this is over,
The price we pay.

Gary Lynch

Ride The Storm

This virus expresses some kind of concern,
Enough to make your thoughts burn,
Don't let this virus get on top of you,
Before you know it the skies will be blue.

We are in a period where lives are lost,
For now we are counting the cost,
The NHS are doing their best,
In a mighty battle in a given test

When it is over I will crack open a beer,
And all the world will openly cheer,
For now be positive and ride the storm
Until the time when things are normal.

Mark Gittings

Love

It sometimes takes a while to realise what you have, we
don't see the time that work and chores take up and just
the fact that you're a mum.
But now there's time to stop and think of everything we
have, my children, my parents, my friends, my pets, the stuff
that makes us live.
If nothing else we've learnt from this, I'll always remember
this, I love my life, I love my kids, I love my family, I love my
pets. Once all this is over I hope I remember this.

Sarah Devine

Reasons To Share

I dreamed a dream the other night
my boat had sailed and I had missed it.
I woke as night turned into day
to find I hadn't risked it.

I hadn't sent the last draft off.
Didn't blog, Facebook or Twitter.
No one could read what I just wrote
so why should I feel bitter

that no one told me I could write
with style and erudition.
How could they know if I don't
show them what I've written.

Christine Campbell

Hope

Life is hard
And life is brutal
Life has hard choices
Some are for the better
Others are for the worse
Regretful decisions
And painful choices

But what if we unite together
During these hard times
We can heal our hearts
And change the world
Make no wrong choice
And you may be known
As a hero in our hearts
Please consider this
As I want you to be there
When this is over.

Lucie Prosser

Twenty-Four-Hour Warriors

It's an early wake-up call,
Where I'm in a rush without breakfast,
I'm half awake and half asleep and my pager always going
bleep bleep bleep.

I'm wondering what challenges I face, as I park in the car
park and out I get in a race.
My duties involve patience,
My duties involve care,
My duties are endless but I'm dedicated to saving lives.
Remember us through the tribulations and the strives.
We are nurses and midwives.

Chantal Anthony

Thank You NHS

I would like to thank you,
you have done a remarkable job,
you have saved life after life .

You went the extra mile,
Finding the light in darkest of times .

You're a family, a friend and a great treasure to our world
Let the rainbow shine upon us
For you have given each and every one of us strength
You're more than just the NHS
You're a special light of society.

Leanne Drain

Thank You

Thanks for looking after us when we're feeling blue,
Even though it's a lot of work for you.
Up and down the country with this virus people are sad,
We want you to know it won't always be this bad.
We thank you and appreciate all that you do
We respect all that you do in your role
We know that making our families and friends better is your goal.
Thank you NHS!

Liz Cotterill

Answer

I'll be home in the spring
If you're going to give me a ring or ping it's not a sin.
I'll be home for Easter whichever is easier
Send me a letter I'll feel much better.
I'm home alone but I'm not going to moan and groan,
If I call I hope I hear your voice after the dialling tone.
We are not alone please pick up the phone.
We are all at home.

Danielle Allen

Like A War Without Bombs

I never really could believe
Through my time of living
That I would see a silent war
So cruel and unforgiving

I cannot see my enemy
Nor smell, not even feel
I only know its energy
And know that it is real

In this war it takes one touch
No bomb will ever be used
This explosive virus grows with lust
It needs to be defused.

Rosemary Wise

Brave For Us

The COVID-19 war approaches us, a silent and invisible invasion. We separate from each other physically. It hurts to remain indoors, to have a limit of freedoms taken for granted, but the bravest of us, the nurses and doctors, stand in the trenches of this invisible enemy healing with unconditional care. You are the bravest of us and I just want to say thank you.

Natalie Brookes

Pull Together

We need to pull together in times like this,
When all you want is a hug or kiss

Let's pull together and leave some space,
And at the end we still see their face

We will pull together and get this done,
Then we shall celebrate with everyone

Take care, be fair, let's share, come on
Pull together, be forever and rebuild as one.

Claire Percival

General Operative

The year's 2020
It started with a blast
Suddenly we blinked
Lives were over fast
Nations stood together
And rallied in support
To show the new disease
That it could be fought
We separated, isolated, quarantined apart
To save the world together
My family and yours

Alex Boal

Blue Days

Some days are blue days
When nothing goes your way
Like winter storm clouds rolling in
And the swallows fly away

Remember though that blue days
Are never all that long
As the sun returns to fill our lives
With joy and swallow song.

Louise Tarn

Stay At Home, Save Lives

Now that we are all apart,
I feel we are more together.
We all just want to go outside
To enjoy the sunny weather.
But, to save the lives of those we love,
We can all surely sacrifice.
Stay inside, stay at home,
It really does save lives.

Shereen

My Wife (A Nurse)

I see no spirit in the sky
I see no hope I can not touch
I feel the love inside living eyes
I feel the hands holding me up
And in the dawn tomorrow
Shall shine another light
To bear away the sorrow
To bring your heart to mine.

Kevin Francis

In The Garden

Sitting in the garden
Reading my favourite book

Hearing the bees buzzing
Seeing the birds swoop

The clouds are fluffy
And the breeze is cool

Oh how the sun is shining
And my little heart is glowing.

Gemma Sykes

A Limerick In Lockdown

For the summer the world could be closed
To make sure that no more are exposed
To a cough-causing germ
That has cut short school terms
And a ban on normal life imposed.

Katy

Because I'm Bored

Why are you watching that?
Why are you eating that?
Why are you reading that?
Why are you sleeping on that?
Why are you writing that?
Because I'm bored.

Josh Waterhouse

Embrace Your Life

There is not a lot
you can do
about your situation
but there is a lot
you can do with
your life.

Natasha Sherman

Brighter Days Ahead

A haiku

after the rainstorm
a rainbow adorns the sky
goodbye Corona.

Samantha Cheshire

WRITE TO UNITE WAS BROUGHT TO YOU BY YOUNG WRITERS

We hope you have enjoyed reading this book — and that you will continue to in the coming years.

If you're a young writer who enjoys reading and creative writing, or the parent of an enthusiastic poet or story writer, do visit our website **www.youngwriters.co.uk**. Here you will find free competitions, workshops and games, as well as recommended reads, a poetry glossary and our blog. There's lots to keep budding writers motivated to write!

If you would like to order further copies of this book, or any of our other titles, then please give us a call or order via your online account.

Young Writers
Remus House
Coltsfoot Drive
Peterborough
PE2 9BF
(01733) 890066
info@youngwriters.co.uk

We're delighted that £1 from every sale of a Write To Unite book is donated to NHS Charities Together Registered Charity No 1186569

Join in the conversation!
Tips, news, giveaways and much more!

 YoungWritersUK    @YoungWritersCW